One day Bean sees a giant
spider go into the shed.

He tells Jelly about the giant
spider. She peeps in the shed.
She will not go in.

The cats tell Wellington and
Kevin about the giant spider.
They all go to look at it.

Wellington and Kevin peep
at the giant spider but they
will not go into the shed.

Lotty comes to look at the
giant spider. She runs away
from it.

Kevin tells the big pig about the giant spider. He goes in the shed.

He goes up to the spider's
web and he sticks his snout
in it.

He grabs the giant spider.

Crunch! Gulp! Oh no! He is

eating the giant spider.

This book focusses on the following vowel graphemes

ay: day   away

ee: sees   peeps

ea: Bean   eating

long i: spider   giant

oe: goes

oo: look

ou: about   snout   out

er: spider

Learn to read with us at Follifoot Farm

Early Vowel Combinations Series

ISBN 978-1-84305-553-2

www.follifootfarm.co.uk

Brown Cow

Book 1
English Vowels Set 2
Author: Marlene Greenwood
Illustrator: Marlene Greenwood

St Chad's RC Primary
Sedgley

Published by Jelly and Bean Ltd
Unit 4A, Follifoot Ridge Business Park
Pannal Road
Harrogate
North Yorkshire
HG3 1DP
www.jellyandbean.co.uk

Copyright 2008 Marlene Greenwood

ISBN 978 1 84305 133 6

Formerly ISBN 978 1 903377 70 3 Down the Lane

MV1

One day Kevin and Lotty are

going to play on the rocks.

They go down the road until they

come to a gate.

1

'Moo ... moo ... moo.' Oh no!

A brown cow is on the grass

behind the hedge.

'Moo ... moo ... moo.'

Kevin does not like cows. He will

not go past it. So the little dogs

keep going down the road.

They come to a gap in the

hedge. They can see the rocks.

'Let's run to the rocks,' says

Lotty.

'Grrr ... grrr ... grrr.'

A big brown dog is behind the

hedge. 'Grrr ... grrr... grrr.'

Kevin does not like big dogs.

He will not go past the big brown

dog. So the little dogs keep going

down the road.

Soon they come to some trees.

They can see the rocks.

'Let's run to the rocks,' says

Lotty.

'Whoo, whoo, whoooooooo.'

A brown owl comes down from

a tree. Kevin runs away.

Lotty is cross with Kevin now.

She runs off to the rocks to have

fun by herself.

Kevin sits down on the grass. He
sees a brown cow, a brown dog
and a brown owl. Oh no! What
will Kevin do now?

'ow'

cow

now

down

brown

owl

soft 'g'

hedge

Other Vocabulary:

Phase 2:   on a is not dogs gap in can run big
off fun and rocks let's sits it

Phase 3:   will with Kevin

Phase 4:   past from cross grass

Vowel Digraphs:

ay: day play says away (gate)

ee: see trees keep

oo: moo soon

oa: road

Tricky words:

to the go no he she they are have one some
come little what oh so do does going like by
herself

Others:

Lotty behind until gate